Ada learns beekeeping at home
with her mother
Alexandra

The Beekeeper & the Bee

Kate Lynch

The Beekeeper & the

Bee

Kate Lynch

Paintings, drawings and the
voices of Somerset beekeepers

First published in 2012 by Furlong Fields Publishing
Illustrations © Kate Lynch 2012
www.katelynch.co.uk

ISBN 978 0 9544394 4 6

Words recorded by Kate Lynch and edited with the beekeepers
Design and layout by Lyn Davies Design
Printed and bound in England by Hamptons, Bristol
Photography of artwork by Delmar Studio, Taunton

FRONT COVER   *Adding a super for the flow*

HALF-TITLE PAGE   *Mid-winter meeting, Heatherton Park*

TITLE PAGE   *Telling the bees*

RIGHT   *Reading a frame of bees*

BACK COVER   *Honey bee on snowdrop*

Contents

FOREWORD *by Martha Kearney*

Since ancient times human beings have been fascinated by honey bees. This was written by Virgil two thousand years ago.

They alone know a country, and a settled home,
and in summer, remembering the winter to come,
undergo labour, storing their gains for all.
For some supervise the gathering of food, and work
in the fields to an agreed rule: some, walled in their homes,
lay the first foundations of the comb, with drops of gum
taken from narcissi, and sticky glue from tree-bark,
then hang the clinging wax: others lead the mature young,
their nation's hope, others pack purest honey together,
and swell the cells with liquid nectar:
there are those whose lot is to guard the gates,
and in turn they watch out for rain and clouds in the sky,
or accept the incoming loads, or, forming ranks,
they keep the idle crowd of drones away from the hive.
The work glows, and the fragrant honey is sweet with thyme. *

The work of the bee has remained largely unchanged through the centuries. The winter is spent with the colony huddled together for warmth against the cold. On sunny days they are tempted out and that is always the cause of relief for the beekeeper. I give my bees sugar fondant to keep the colony going during the long months when they are unable to forage. Come spring, the bees emerge more frequently, combing nearby fields and gardens for vital pollen and nectar. I can spend hours just watching my bees, transfixed by their labours. May and June is the season of the swarm, when bees create more colonies – and often stress for the beekeeper. I once found myself climbing a very wobbly hawthorn tree to try to capture a swarm. The book contains a lovely description of weaving a skep, the traditional basket used to catch runaway bees. Then comes the sticky season when honey extraction takes place and every surface of the house gets covered in the stuff. With the autumn, the hives need feeding up again for the winter ahead and so the year begins once more.

Kate Lynch's drawings and paintings are delightful and I only wish I looked as calm and graceful as her beekeepers do. The best artistic representation of me would be a cartoon of a panicky woman being chased by her bees after making some elementary error! It is reassuring to see that the beekeepers of Somerset are a superior breed, and I hope you enjoy their own descriptions of the year.

In recent times though, the old ways of the honey bee have been disrupted by a number of diseases. The worst threat is the varroa mite, a bloodsucker which feeds off baby bees. It weakens the colonies and leaves them prey to all sorts of viruses. There are other threats too as wildflower habitats disappear. The result is that a substantial number of hives are dying out each year in this country. Research is being carried out to discover more about the causes and try to find solutions. Bees pollinate vast quantities of our crops, so their decline is not only serious for beekeepers but for our farmers and food supply too.

But enough gloom. Just relish this beautiful record of the beekeeping year and marvel at the industry of these intriguing little creatures.

MARTHA KEARNEY
Beekeeper, broadcaster & patron of
Bees for Development

* Virgil *Georgics* Book IV,*c.*29 BC, translated by A.S Kline 2002

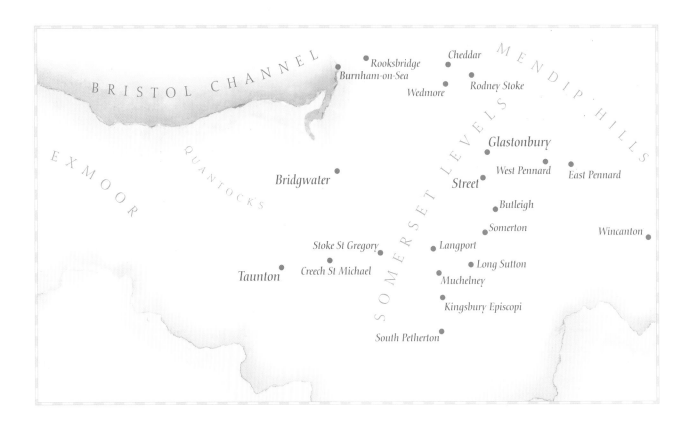

THE SOMERSET LEVELS

The Somerset Levels and Moors cover an area of central Somerset between the Quantocks and the Mendip Hills. The Levels are largely flat coastal areas, drained by man since Domesday and broken up by a few ridges and characteristic 'mumps' (small hills). The Moors are the inland peaty plains. The many thousands of willows on the Levels, planted for the basket maker or edging the 'rhines' (drainage ditches), are valuable spring forage for bees. The beekeepers featured in the book mainly live on slightly raised land in and around the floodplain. This is old cider country and there are still many acres of orchards, with gallons of farmhouse 'scrumpy' produced. Farms in Somerset have traditionally been small, with a mixture of crops and livestock. There is an abundance of unimproved pastureland and meadows with carpets of nectar-rich dandelions and other wild flowers, also miles of hedgerows full of bee fodder – blackthorn, hawthorn and delicious flowering brambles. For the more adventurous beekeeper there are significant arable areas growing favourable crops and the temptation of an outing up to the heather on Exmoor in late summer.

Smoking the bees

JANUARY

The winter cluster

If we have a hard winter the bees stay tightly clustered inside the hive. The hives look dormant, but it's not what it seems. The bees are working to keep the cluster at an even temperature, vibrating their wing muscles to produce heat, that goes on all the time so none of them freeze.

If we get a mild winter they'll break cluster and come out of the hive and fly around, but there's nothing out there for them, so they're just using up energy and they'll have to eat more of their stores. That's when you have to keep a close eye on them. It's surprising how few colonies of bees get through the winter in the wild. When it's a hard winter they stand a better chance of a survival because they're not flying and using up too much of their precious winter stores.

It's a shame there isn't more beekeeping at school – that's where I got my first interest, at junior school. The headmaster kept bees and I always remember the whole school was called out one day to watch him taking a swarm and that's what started it all for me. You're impressionable at that age aren't you and there's so much that's fascinating with bees.

Gerald Fisher

The bees need about 35 pounds of honey for the winter to see them through from September to March. That's why we heft the hive at the end of the season, September-time, to judge how much they've got in store, and probably again after Christmas. We can tell if there's enough by the weight, lifting it up just on the one corner, hefting we call it.

I'll give them candy end of January, I always do it as a matter of routine. And again in March, but a lot depends on the weather – if you get a mild winter they eat a lot. They cluster if it's cold and then they don't eat much, but if it's mild they're still active. During the winter they don't sleep, bees never sleep, they don't hibernate, they fly all winter – they keep the hive clean, they have to go outside to relieve themselves and they have to feed and keep warm and keep the cluster going. Beekeepers understand what's going on in the hive. The cluster moves around the hive, you can usually tell where it is, you can see a dry patch on the outside and you hope all is well in the hive. The queen doesn't lay eggs from September till January, she just wanders around and the bees feed her, then she'll start laying, building up the colony for the summer.

Neil Trood

Feeding the bees

FEBRUARY & MARCH

First pollen

The other day they came out for just about three quarters of an hour, it warmed up just enough, I looked at one hive and you'd have thought they were swarming, then it clouded over and they were all in again. It's a very small window at this time of year when they may come out, the temperature has to be nearer to 14 degrees, although sometimes, if it's a really sunny day but colder, they may come out. I've seen them fly on a very bright day when there's snow on the ground, the brightness of the snow brings them out, I've seen them collecting water on snow.

At this time of year they'll come out for the pollen in snowdrops and the crocuses if it's warm enough. They're starting to build up the colony and the pollen is for the brood. It's difficult to know how the bees are doing – whether they've survived the winter. You daren't open the hives yet, it's not warm enough, so you're watching to see if they're flying on a sunny day.

Tom Done

Honey bee on snowdrop

Honey bee on crocus

This time of year they're going crazy for food, there's been nothing coming in over the winter, they're running low on stores. Sometimes the bees will be out just collecting pollen and you'll see them chewing it off the flowers' anthers, but otherwise they'll dive right in to sip the nectar and they get covered in the pollen as they're doing it. Then you'll see them brushing it off with the pollen brushes they have on their hind legs – they can get their legs round to their mouths so they'll brush it, chew it up and squidge it in this special pollen press they have between the joints of their hind legs. Then it gets extruded up into these two rows of long hairs on their back legs and in the middle there's a spike and the pollen gathers around this spike, it's called the pollen basket – and they just keep adding to this and they get huge amounts. If you look at them it's huge blocks of the same coloured pollen on their knees – they're mostly working one kind of flower at a time. Then, back in the hive, the bee with the pollen goes and packs it herself, goes up to a cell and takes the load off. She scrapes it off with her back legs, shoves it into the cell with her mouth and, once the cell's full, then she's back out foraging again. The house bees do the next bit. They come and mix up the pollen in the cells, chew it up and make it into a paste, stick it back into the cell and cap it over – it's bee bread, food for the new brood.

Eleanor Rose Burgess

Honey bee on hellebore

They need loads of pollen for the grubs, it's the protein. That's why they're out at this time of year, and that's why it's so good having hazel around because it's such a boost of pollen they can collect in a short amount of time. The winter heath is coming in, that's a browny-orange pollen, whereas the crocus pollen is bright orange. It's beautiful to see all the different coloured pollen in the hive. They've been working the winter aconites, they're just about over. Hellebores they're working, and daffodils are coming out, they've been working them this year, and the violets. I've never seen them working violets, but they are this year, something's going on, maybe they're producing nectar this year when normally they don't, it all depends on the weather. Catkins don't produce nectar but they have so much pollen – bees love catkins, they get absolutely coated in pollen and you see them there grooming themselves and doing a strange little dance, brushing the pollen off and collecting it on their back legs. They'll be collecting nectar too – primroses they've been working and the lungwort and the bell heathers, they get nectar off those. Any sunny day they'll be out.

Eleanor Rose Burgess

APRIL

Opening the hive

It's the start of the season. You check through all the hives to see how they're doing. Sometimes you lose a couple of colonies, they didn't make it through the winter, they had diseases or weren't strong enough. You check them through as soon as it's more than 12 degrees – they usually start working at 12 degrees – then at 14 degrees you go through them. You don't want them getting chilled. We'll check to see if there are eggs and larvae, whether the queen is active and laying.

It hit the right temperature last week and we did open up a couple of hives a few days ago. We had something quite interesting - one of them had no queen, the queen had gone, died probably, and the colony can't last without a queen. Anyway, we opened up the next hive and it was empty, frame after frame, no bees at all, then on the last frame we checked we found two lone bees and there was a queen – strange, just two bees and one queen! So we put the queen in a queen cage, it's a little perforated box, and we put some fondant sugar as a bung in the end and put her in the other hive which didn't have a queen. By the time the queen eats her way out and the bees have also fed her she should have the hive smell and the bees will accept her as their queen. This is the hive here, and we have to see if she survived. If the bees don't accept a queen they'll kill her. It's looking good, the bees are carrying pollen into the hive, you can see their back legs packed with it, that's a good sign. We'll open it up now. Look, there's new brood in the cells, and eggs, I can see eggs. The queen is laying. There are grubs and they're feeding them – we've re-queened the colony, I'm really pleased.

Eleanor Rose Burgess

MAY

The spring flow

The queen in here is a veteran, she's four years old. I don't often name a queen, but I call her Doris in recognition of her long service. She's a bit of a legend, a nice big queen – she could peg it any moment, but she's still laying. I can see eggs, I can see she's doing fine, lots of brood. The most amazing thing is she's still laying. Technically she should have run out of eggs and sperm already.

The queen has a shiny, longer abdomen, pointed at the tail. She's big, but not so fat as the drones – they're the boys. She's longer, more linear, but it's not always as obvious as you might think. She also tends to have red legs. When you try to find her she'll be ducking and diving to find a dark place to go. Some queens are quite skittish, they can really leg it. This lot aren't flying much, quite a nice docile colony of bees and in quite a good mood, they're not aggressive at all.

In warm weather, when you've got a flow on, the worker bees – they're the girls – well they produce wax like you and I perspire. They secrete wax naturally, and they'll dump it if there isn't space for them to draw comb. What we tend to do is give them enough room – idle hands make swarming bees! These boxes are the supers and when you first put a super on you're not putting it on just for honey, you're putting it on to give the bees room as the queen is upping her egg production – they'll want room to draw comb for their honey stores.

Pat Lehain

Pat adding a super

There's Michelins in this orchard, and Dabinetts – Dabinetts have been around for quite a few years, they're a little bit of a sweeter apple than the Michelins. We grow about 30 or 40 different varieties, and we've got pears and plums. We've been cider makers since 1840. This orchard's been in our family since the 1920s. Grandfather made a fair bit of cider during the war, cider was very popular then, there wasn't much beer made during the war.

There's always been bees in the orchards in my time, and Father said when he was a nipper there were always bees. Father never kept bees himself. Fred Higgins had bees out here – all the old-timers used to keep them out here. John Talbot was the last chap, and when he gave up I took over.

That's a little hive up in that tree in case a swarm might go in there – a bait hive – sometimes you get a swarm comes out and they might go in there. Some people mow the dandelions off so the bees go for the blossom not the dandelions, but we've only started mowing today so we didn't mow the dandelions. The bees just go for what they want out here. There are eight hives in this orchard, so there's plenty, they can do their work. Then there's clover for them later in the season when it comes out, clover's nice. We keep bees just for the apples, for the fruit. We're not keeping them for the honey, we're keeping them for the pollination and the honey's a bonus, it helps, and it pays for any kit you have to buy. I get a real good crop of apples out here, always do, it's good, you've got to have bees in your orchard.

Andrew Hecks

Honey bee on apple blossom

Reading a frame in the rape field

The farmer likes me to come in with the bees when there's rape, and he's got beans next, they'll be good, probably end of May if there's good growing weather. It increases the yield and the quality if there's pollination. Years ago – 20 or 25 years ago – the rape grew above your head. It used to yield nectar like billio, they used the stalks then, as a straw for bedding. It's stumpy now, a lot different, interfered with. It's a good honey, rape, I make it into soft-set honey. It crystallizes very quickly though, once you take it off – not in the hive because in the hive it's the right temperature, but once you take it off it crystallizes very fast and you have to get the honey out within a few days or it'll need to be melted down.

I'm just checking the hives, seeing what's happening. You can see the brood here in the centre of this frame, see the eggs, the queen's laying well. Here's a tiny grub hatched out, probably two to three days old, a tiny c-shape. See the glistening stuff it's sat on – looks a bit like condensed milk – that's the royal jelly, all the bees get some, the workers get a mustard spoonful, whereas to make a new queen they'll feed her about a tablespoonful. Then here are some older grubs, nice and fat and juicy, and here are some that are capped – they're the sealed brood, they'll be pupating into bees. When they emerge they'll need to eat pollen, so here are the pollen stores nearby, you can see the deep orange, that's dandelion pollen, and the paler yellow, that's the rape. The pollen's like the baby food, it's placed near the brood cells, for the new bees when they emerge. Then the nectar and honey are further away on the perimeter of the frame. It's all logical. These bees are very docile, they're the nurse bees – the young bees – and when they emerge they feed the grubs and do the household chores. They don't go out foraging until they're three weeks old.

Eddie Howe

Honey bees on allium

I grow mostly perennials – they get their feet down deep and do very well. I love the alliums, bees really work them, they love purple and yellows, the colours that are out at the beginning of the year when nectar's so important. They love herbs – thyme, comfrey, catmint, all the salvias and sage family – and laburnum. They like simple flowers, open flowers. Often petals will have ultra-violet markings which we can't see but the bees can, they guide the bee into the centre of the flower. What the bees don't like are fancy double flowers, flowers that have been bred with frilly petals, they just can't get through them – peonies and chrys-anthemums are difficult for them to get into and most roses aren't much good, but singles are fine. Cotoneaster is one of the best producers, each flower releases a tiny drop of nectar, but a lot of little drops make a full honey stomach. The cabbage has gone over, I thought I'd leave it, they love cabbage flowers, yellow again, I'll just chop them down before the seeds spill out.

Vicky Andrews

When the bees are out foraging and they find a good nectar yielder they may mark it with a pheromone, then when they get back to the hive they'll do this dance to tell the other bees generally which way to go and how far, then when the other bees get close they'll be able to pick up the pheromone marker. Such clever little beasts. The forager dumps the nectar as soon as she can back in the hive, spews it out of her mouth, then the hive bees move it to where it's supposed to be and reduce it by fanning their wings. When the bees arrive back at the hive you know the ones with their honey stomachs full of nectar, they land heavily, they hit the deck a bit hard sometimes!

Terry Andrews

The bees are tetchy today, I knew they would be, they really do not like this overcast weather, the guard bees are out.

I usually go through the hives every seven days or so. The bees don't need me to look after them, but you want to check for disease and also if you don't go through them you run the risk of losing swarms. If they make a new queen they'll swarm. You lose half of your workforce and they take as much honey as they can to set up home somewhere else.

Can you see they're busy going down into the honey cells, that's because they've smelt the smoke, they think their home might be on fire, they're filling up with honey in case they have to leave. That's why we use the smoker, keeps the bees busy, distracts them.

Now, in this hive I'll be very surprised if I find queen cells because at the beginning of the season I found two queens in here, which is very unusual – mother and daughter working side by side – but it'll only be for a very short period, then they get rid of the old queen and keep the new one. The new queen is somewhere in the brood nest – good, there she is! And here's horse-chestnut pollen, deep red, wine-coloured, they normally keep different pollen separate. And, glistening in the cells, that's nectar, it hasn't been reduced yet to make it into honey, they fan it with their wings, evaporate the water in it. Then those bigger domed cells, they're the drone brood, but I'm looking for queen cells – they're larger, they hang down, you can't miss them and if they cap one it's a sure sign they'll swarm. It's one of the wonders of nature what goes on in here.

Gerald Fisher

Opening the hive

JUNE

A silver spoon

When the bees swarm there's a lot of activity before they go, they mill around, and then suddenly they all get together and vroom, it's like an aeroplane, a tremendous noise – you hear a swarm before you see it. They fly together at quite a speed and they know exactly where they are going, the scouts have decided. They don't necessarily find their final destination straightaway though, it might take a few goes.

This swarm was hanging about on a branch in a garden. It was a big swarm, a tremendous weight, but very stable. Once they settle there's a soft gentle purring sound, they're very docile. They've gorged on honey before setting out – they have to have enough honey for all that flying and then they have to make a new home, making wax takes a lot of energy. But they are very benign while they wait for the scouts to decide where they go next – a suitable cavity of some sort, an old chimney, a hole in a tree … I'm not worried about swarms. I've never known a bad-tempered swarm. You can't hang about while you take a swarm though, they can go whoosh just like that and they've gone.

With this swarm I clipped some branches to get to it and then knocked it off and it landed in the skep with a big thud. Then I put the skep on the ground the other way up, leaving a little gap so any flying bees could find their way in. So long as the queen's in there, the guard bees fan a pheromone from their tail which says 'come on in, this is where our queen is'.

By the evening there weren't any bees flying, so I wrapped up the skep and put it in the van and took it to a lady who wanted some bees. We hived them that evening. That's one of the wonders, seeing the bees parade into the hive.

Roy White

I got a phone call this morning. There was a swarm in a farmer's hedge, so I drove there straightaway. I shook them into the skep, then went back to collect them this evening. I'll tip them out now and they'll start marching shortly. Yes, there they go, they're going up quickly, that's as fast as I've seen them go. I haven't seen the queen yet, sometimes you can see her marching in. Look, you can see them making a bee chain, lining the path up. It's quite dramatic on the white sheet – it's white because it's the opposite to dark, leads them up to the dark door, they'll always go up to the dark, dark means home.

Can you see that one with its tail up, and another there – the tiny white blob poking out, that's their nazanov gland, and they're fanning. That's to let the others know to come on in, they waft the scent to tell the others 'it's good here'. It's a small colony, a cast probably, not the primary swarm. The primary swarm would have the old queen, a secondary swarm will have a virgin queen and she'll need to mate,

she'll be flying out in the next few days, she'll need to go quite soon. There's only a short time for a virgin queen to get mated, she'll fly out to the drone congregation – where the boys all gather.

The bees are pretty docile at this stage, they haven't got anything to defend so they're unlikely to sting. They've got a lot of work to do now making a new home, drawing out all that comb. Look, they're pretty well all in, a good job done. I'll just tap the skep, shake the last stragglers out. That was quite impressive, that's the best hiving I've seen. I expect they like their new home, they've been hanging about on a branch in the open for a couple of days. A swarm in June is worth a silver spoon – I haven't got any spoons, but we'll take the farmer a pot of honey for the swarm. I'm very pleased.

Daniel Govier

Hiving the swarm

We used to have seven beehives, now we've just got two, we keep them near the pigs. I started going to the bees with my mummy when I was about four, that's when I got my bee suit. And I can go to the Bee Club at school when I'm in Year Five.

I don't mind when the bees buzz round me – they haven't stung me and they usually fly over my head. My mummy has got stung, and my daddy is allergic so he doesn't go to the bees much. Sometimes people come here before they get bees, they may not like the buzzing, so they come to try it out. We take out a frame and hold it and we try to find the queen. She has a blue mark on her. My mummy has a blue pen and if the queen doesn't have a blue mark she puts one on because the boys can look a bit like the queen so then you can spot her. I get in a bit of a muddle sometimes – sometimes I think it's a queen, but it's a drone. You need to see where the queen is because you don't want her going in the boxes where the honey is. You don't want her laying eggs in the honey.

I think bees are so clever collecting nectar and turning it into honey. They don't even have much of a break from all that flying, except at night. They don't exactly sleep, but they do lie down sometimes when they're tired. It's not really fair taking the honey, but we always leave them some, because they've done all that work making it. I like honey. I like it on my toast, I like it in my yoghurt and when I'm ill it helps my throat.

Ada Ostroumoff

Looking for the queen

JULY

The summer flow and the honey

The weather is everything. Take the lime tree, it only yields nectar when it's thundery and humid, and you only get honey from clover when it's flying ant weather, that heavy heat when you toss and turn and can't sleep. The biggest flow of nectar is usually in July, but it's unpredictable, you still need warmth and there's got to be moisture for their roots. It may be two weeks when the flowers really yield loads of nectar, or three weeks or just one week. You know when it happens – usually it's when the blackberry is in flower – the bees are frantically collecting nectar and bringing it back, coming and going all the time, it's hectic, and you can smell it, it's in the air all around the hive. It's in the air because the house bees have to reduce the nectar down. The flying bees collect the nectar and then the house bees have to turn it into honey. They do it by fanning their wings, so they're inside all fanning like mad, and you've got bees clustered on the outside of the hive, they're all flapping their wings too, they're all trying to create a draught and evaporate the water from the nectar to make honey. It's serious work, and it's the evaporation in the air all around – you don't just have to be standing on top of the hive to smell it, it's everywhere, it's a lovely sweet smell when there's a flow on. That's usually when it happens, when the blackberry is flowering, the bees are getting their stores in to be able to survive the winter.

Neil Trood

Honey bees on blackberry flowers

Taking off a honey super

It's heavy work taking the supers off when they're full of honey. They can weigh up to 28 pounds, and that's nearly all honey. These are from our 'wild bees', well we call them 'wild' because they were a wild colony we caught, but as it happens it's appropriate, they're narky, spoiling for a fight. People say it's the black bees are the nasty ones but these are quite light in colour – they're a fabulous colony though, they produce a lot of honey.

Once we've got the supers off the hives, we take out the frames and slice the caps off. The bees cap each cell once they've reduced the nectar down to honey, so you have to take off the little wax caps, they're wafer thin, and you need to break every single cell or the honey won't come out, but trying to keep as much of the comb as possible. We put all the cappings back to feed to the bees, they'll clean them up, lick all the honey off, then Karen makes candles with the wax.

Chris Strong

Slicing the caps and spinning and straining honey at Beer

When you've sliced the caps off the comb, you can spin out the honey. We just put four frames at a time in the extractor. Your arms ache with the winding and it's better with two of you, one turning and one holding it down. The honey goes straight through the sieve at the bottom and we'll let it settle. We just put it through one more sieve after that to keep its lovely flavour – no processing. This honey, we think, is from the small-leafed lime tree, there are lots round here, and blackberry, and, before that, field thistles, they are very partial to field thistles.

It's been a bumper year, there wasn't much of a June gap, not like last year, last year it was rainy and cold. This year I couldn't keep up. You can't just wait for one of those boxes to be completely filled, and then say 'I'll put another one on', you have to make sure that when they're half-filling one you put another super on. Just think of a washing line – you need to hang your washing to dry, then you can fold it up. Well, the nectar's the washing, it has to be dried out. You've got foragers coming in with nectar and dumping it everywhere, everywhere … and then the house bees they're fanning it to reduce it, and moving it around, filling up cells, fanning, moving, filling, and then, when they've turned it into honey and have a cell full, they cap it. They need loads of room to store it and if they haven't got enough room, then that's when they might swarm.

We'll put the empty frames back in the hive, the bees will clean them up and tidy them and use them again – there's still some blackberry out.

Karen Cox

43

AUGUST

Heather and driving bees

I got involved with bees years ago, in my 20s, but I'd learnt about them before, at school in Rural Studies. Then later I used to milk cows and the gardener in the nearby big house – he was about 85 and not a big chap – he asked if I'd straighten his hives out, they'd been knocked over by sheep. He gave me big gloves, but I still got ten bee stings. The bees weren't happy being knocked over and my hand looked like a cricket bat with five fat pork sausages sticking out of the end. It didn't put me off though.

I usually take some hives up on Exmoor at the end of July. By the time we get to heather time, it's all finished down below, we're spinning out the summer honey. It's always nice to come up here for an afternoon when you've been spinning honey all morning, check the bees, bring lunch, it's a different world, moist and green. You can smell the heather in the wind, it's got that sweet pungent smell, bitter-sweet. Ling honey's lovely on a piece of nice fresh bread with clotted cream. The ling's the deep pink with bell flowers, it's pretty well finished – and the bell heather's almost over. It's been dry this year for heather. They say you need a wet May and plenty of sun. Heather likes wet feet and a warm head.

Chris Harries

Nowadays we mainly take honey from extra boxes we put on the hive. They're called supers and house removable frames which the bees fill with comb and honey. We always make sure enough stores remain for the bees though, and keep a close eye on them.

Before the system of removable frames was developed, people in this country largely kept bees in skeps made of straw. When it came to taking the honey, the bees were killed by placing the skep over a sulphur pit. The burning sulphur suffocated the bees and killed them. It was very rough and ready, rather a cruel and inefficient practice. It wasn't realised that the bees could be re-housed and fed, thus saving their lives. Some enlightened people discovered how to drive the bees out of the skep, so that they could take the honey without destroying the bees. Of course they had to feed them with sugar to keep them alive through the winter, but at least they weren't killed. Certain young men used to go off to farmers and cottage beekeepers asking if they could drive their bees for them. I think it must have been a good Sunday afternoon outing a hundred years ago or so – they would accumulate the driven bees to take back home with them, and I have a nice old photograph of them carrying baskets of bees on their bicycles.

I learnt how to drive bees when I was a young man. You drum on the side of the hive and the bees march up into an empty skep you place there. You keep up the rhythm and they all leave, then you've just got a skep full of comb and honey without any bees. Do it at the right time – probably end of August or September when there are no grubs – and the honeycomb is clean and ready to eat. For beekeeping exams years ago everyone had to be able to drive bees, and to get top marks you had to spot the queen on her ascent!

David Charles

46

Driving bees

SEPTEMBER & OCTOBER

Apples, ivy and mead

We pick all the apples by hand, up a ladder or shaking the tree. If the hives are nearby we can shut the bees up for a time. You get used to working round the bees and they get used to you working too.

We've taken off the honey and now it's time to check the bees have got enough stores for the winter and treat them for the varroa mite. I put wire round the hives this time of year, that will hopefully stop the woodpeckers. We had a lot of problems last winter, it was a hard one and woodpeckers must have been struggling for food because they went for the hives and did a lot of damage. They eat bees and grubs – once they bore their way through their tongues can reach a long way in. I'll be closing up the entrance now so the mice can't get in this winter. Oh, the mice love to get in if they can, they make a nest in the hive and eat away the comb, they can wipe out a whole colony and ruin the brood chamber. And I'll be tying up the hives, so if a badger did come along and knock one over – or there's a gale – they stay intact.

I always had a dream of being a sort of peasant farmer one day, and that's what we are really. Everything's all intertwined, like it was in the past – the bees and fruit and the grass and sheep and the honey and the cider, then we feed the pomace to the sheep and pigs through the winter. Everything's interlinked, but sadly the old circle's got broken with modern farming.

Colin Comben

Apple harvest at Honeypot Farm

The drones have already gone – the girls kick them out in September – and the queen's not laying much now. Numbers are down in the hive, from 50,000 to maybe 20,000, and there will only be a few thousand by Christmas.

The bees are on the ivy today, the flowers have a horrid smell, but that doesn't bother them, they'll be collecting the pollen and the nectar, it's their last food for their winter stores. The ivy nectar's high in glucose and in time the honey goes rock hard in the hive, but it's a good food for them till it granulates. Ivy is a very valuable plant for the bees – don't chop your ivy down!

The bees are nearly ready for the winter. They are growing these little fat bodies now – they take on fat for energy, they're physically different from the summer bees. In the spring and summer they just live for six weeks, but these winter bees have got to survive the whole winter until the queen starts laying again. Now they're getting in the last of their winter stores, they've done their house-keeping, and anything that needs sealing up they've sealed up. They're like us, settling into our nice warm kitchen – the difference is they've got to keep their hive warm them-selves. They'll form a cluster and flap their wings to get up heat. Being cold-blooded, they have to work very hard all winter flexing their muscles to keep their hive at 34 degrees, so they'll need a good supply of honey for energy.

Roy White

Ivy, the last forage

Racking mead

Honey goes back thousands of years, it was always special, and both honey and mead were used in religious ceremonies and medicine. Only honey that hasn't been properly evaporated by the bees will start to ferment and fizz in the jar. Fermentation won't happen with a mature good honey, you have to water down a good honey to ferment it – so most people don't use it to make mead now.

These days you tend to make mead from the residue of the honey harvest in the autumn. You land up with a bucket full of high-class 'gunk' – wax cappings, honey, bees knees and other bits all mixed up – although the wax and honey in it are still valuable. The first stage is to separate the honey from the wax. I make up a big vat of the gunk with water warm enough to dissolve the honey- not boiling or it will melt the wax and ruin the delicate flavours. You strain it and add some more honey if it needs it to get to the right specific gravity. Then we add yeast and a few traces of nutrients and off it goes … to become mead if you're lucky! But sometimes

the fermentation stops – mead is rather prone to sticking. It's a sort of alchemy. All this happens in the autumn usually, although the end of the beekeeping year is getting later and later. It's shifted, it's warmer now. Fifty years ago they bedded hives down for the winter earlier than we do.

Today I'm racking off the mead I made a year ago but it'll be a few years before it's ready to drink. We can taste a bottle from 2007 – it's a sweet mead. I won a prize for it at the Honey Show last year. Dry mead takes longer to mature but even then I find it 'thin' and it can have a slightly antiseptic edge. Sweet mead is rounder. That's what mead's all about, you want to feel the honey in it. It's all a bit of fun. I can be out here for hours, brewing away and sampling. That's the best bit – regular sampling to make sure it's maturing nicely!

Alex Morrice

53

NOVEMBER & DECEMBER

Wax, weaving and the wing of a goose

They have a weird smell these old honeycombs, almost sour, and some of them are black – they're black because the bees do a lot of walking on them and their feet are dirty. Also, the sides of the cells become dark and shiny. The queen goes in again and again and lays her eggs, and the larvae spin cocoons and pupate, and the house bees get rid of most of it but not all, and then they polish up the cells each time with the propolis. These old combs are actually amazingly heavy, there's lots of dross, more cocoon than wax sometimes, and they're toughened with the propolis. It's amazing stuff, propolis – I expect if you were in a wood watching you could see the bees get it from where the tree is bleeding. They catch hold of it with their mandibles and take it back to the hive. They use it for all sorts of things – cleaning, polishing, sealing gaps, sticking and glueing. I chip some off and make a tincture and sell it sometimes. It's got lots of healing properties.

I try to keep taking old wax off frames as a winter job. There may not be much honey left in the old combs, but the bees smell it from a long way off if it's warm, and they'll soon be buzzing round. So you need a cool day to get the wax out, but then you need a nice sunny one to melt it in the solar extractor. There's a lot of work that's away from the hive, that's for sure. I prefer to take the old wax out every three years or so, turn the frames over – it's a good way of getting rid of disease, and getting the bees to draw out new comb is a good way to keep them in the hive, gives them all something to do.

I'll pack all this old wax into ladies' stockings. It's a sticky business and there's nothing exotic about stuffing honeycomb into ladies stockings – it always creates a bit of laughter in my family – but there's no better strainer! Then I'll throw the filled stockings in the solar extractor and off you go – all the dross is left in the stockings and the melted wax runs clear. I probably strain it twice more, through cotton. I make hand cream and it has to be pristine. That's another winter job. And making candles – I love beeswax candles.

Roy White

Eleanor washing frames

Early winter is a busy time. We make candles, soap and balms with the beeswax. There's also all the hive work – cleaning, sterilising, repairing and storing equipment – and we try to get that done by Christmas. The bees can re-use their honeycomb for a few years, but eventually the comb gets dirty and old – you can tell by the look of it, it goes dark, it's just the age of the wax. You're trying to do your best by the bees and you don't want to give them back old comb which they wouldn't use naturally in the wild. At a certain point they want fresh comb. So when we realise it's too old, we scrape out the wax – we can reclaim a lot of this – and then we get out the Burco boiler and boil up a big vat of water mixed with washing soda. Once it's really hot you dip the frames in and get a brush and scrape off any residual wax and leave them to dry. Then you put new foundation on in the spring. We do it once a year. It doesn't matter how cold it is outside, you've got this vat boiling away and it keeps you warm in the shed.

There are wonderful smells – the washing soda's the old fashioned cleaning fluid and it's boiling away, and mixed in you've got the propolis – that's the tree resin the bees collect, they coat everything in the hive with the propolis and it soaks into the wood – and you've got the sweet wax and honey smells in the steam too – it's lovely.

By this time of year you've fed the bees and they've got enough food, you've made sure the hives are sound, with enough ventilation so they won't get damp, and now the bees should be nicely tucked up in their cluster keeping themselves warm – keeping their queen, and as many bees as they can, alive through the winter. If it's a mild winter the bees are more active – they need food if they're active and, with no forage about, what the beekeeper and the bees need is a short cold winter rather than a long mild one.

Eleanor Rose Burgess

The straw comes from the Wrights who are thatchers in Compton Dundon, it's their straw, they grow it. It's wheat straw, it makes a strong basket. The guide is a slice of cow horn – that's how the straw is packed tight to coil it – and, once you've started, you keep it filled up with straw, not too wet, but damp and pliable. Then I'm using the traditional needle, it's a turkey leg bone – it's not a needle exactly, but it makes a channel for the stitch. They used to use blackberry in Somerset for the stitching – the long streamers that grow over the summer – they'd strip the thorns off and split it and scrape out the pith. I've had a go but it's a bit time-consuming! I'm using chairmakers' lapping cane. You stitch the coils diagonally and lock each stitch into the one in the coil underneath, that gives the diagonal pattern and makes it strong. At the end you tail off, let the straw peter out and bind the top edge.

They needed lots of skeps a hundred years ago, then all their bees were kept in them. Now we use them just for catching swarms. They weren't that weatherproof though, so they made hackles for them which were like tall straw hats, or sometimes they put an upturned cream bowl on top, or there were bee boles, which were cubby holes in walls – that's how they kept them dry.

It was probably a winter thing, skep-making, like cleaning up the frames, sorting out the hives and making candles. You can go on weaving in the twilight – dumpsey light a friend of mine calls it – they did so much in the half-light and by candlelight or firelight in those days.

Sometimes I find I'm more pleased with a skep I've made later – at the time you see the faults, then you put it away and when you look at it later you think, 'well that's not too bad'. This one will have taken me nearly two and a half days. It's really pleasing when it's done, if it's a nice shape.

Diana Robertson

Weaving a bee skep

It's my second year rearing geese, I had seven last year, 26 this year. My bees are in the orchard and do a good job pollinating the apple blossom and then the apples feed the geese, it's a good combination. The geese ate loads of apples, cleared away all the windfalls and I haven't had to mow the grass – they reckon three geese graze the equivalent of one sheep. I imagine all the cottagers in the old days had bees and chickens, ducks and geese – not turkeys, they're much more modern, a goose was traditional for Christmas. And the honey's nice at Christmas too, I use it on parsnips, honey-roast parsnips, can't beat them, and there's a recipe for honey-basted goose too.

Then a goose's wing makes a good bee brush, for brushing the bees off the frames, or when you're getting the stragglers from a swarm. Bees go crazy when you use a nylon brush, they hate it, maybe it's a bit more prickly, but they don't tend to react nearly so badly with a goose wing. It is soft and just the right shape for a bee brush, pointed, with a good stiff bone. It's always been a traditional bee brush and beekeepers who buy a Christmas goose from me get a bee brush too!

Daniel Govier

Daniel and Peter driving geese

Come December, the bees should have enough to eat and they're in their cluster, it's a bit like a vortex as the bees on the outside burrow their way in when they get cold and the warmer ones are forced out. I heard recently that there may be 'heater bees' in the cluster, they've taken infrared photos and can see some bees glowing like red hot coals, moving about, being fed by others. They are always finding out more about bees.

My interest started years ago – a friend of mine was a beekeeper and they had meetings and there were dear old beekeepers who would talk about bees for a bit and then they would talk about their childhood and the war. It was real old Somerset. And after about five years going to these wonderful meetings and listening to the old bee-keepers, someone said I ought to get some bees, and so I did. Michael wasn't keen because his mother used to have a gardener and he kept bees and they used to swarm up tall trees and poor Aubrey used to have to climb up and get them, but we got some bees anyway, and when we took the lid off Michael was absolutely hooked – we both were. That was 25 years ago.

We don't keep bees just for the honey. It's so fascinating and there are always surprises. At this time of year they may come out on a sunny day for a cleansing flight, and they need to collect water – and it's always good to see. I'm an outdoor person, I'm like the bees, if it's a sunny day I can't stay inside – I like to get out and when I'm out I watch the bees. Once Christmas is over you're looking forward to spring. The bees will be out for the snowdrops and crocuses. Once it's shirt-sleeve weather we can check them over, see how they're doing. When you know your bees are happy all's right with the world.

Christiane Hare

Hives under a winter moon

Glossary

BROOD The eggs, larvae (grubs) and pupating bees in their cocoons.

BROOD BOX The box in which the honey bee queen lays eggs and house bees rear the young - more spacious than the supers, with room for queen, drones, workers, food for day-to-day running of the hive and enough cells for the brood. In winter this is where the queen and the winter cluster live.

CANDY Fondant icing fed to the bees if they are in need of a boost of food.

DRONES The boys. These male bees are only reared at certain times of year. Their only purpose is to mate with virgin queens - and they are built for the job. Honey bees mate while flying, so the drone is equipped with strong

wing muscles. His huge eyes and large antennae help him spot a virgin queen from some distance.

THE FLOW In warm temperatures flowers produce an abundance of sugar-rich nectar to attract bees for vital pollination. When there is a huge influx of honey bee food coming into the hive beekeepers refer to it as 'the flow'.

FORAGERS The older worker bees. Their strong muscles take them from flower to flower and back to the hive with nectar and loads of pollen. They also collect water and propolis when needed.

FRAMES Nowadays beekeepers mainly use hives with movable wooden frames which they fit with sheets of beeswax called foundation. The bees build comb on to this wax. Movable frames enable the modern beekeeper to easily check on the colony through the year and take the honey without damaging the bees.

GRUB The white larva which hatches from the egg in each hexagonal cell, fed and cared for by the house bees until it is fat enough to pupate.

POMACE After pressing the juice from apples, the cider-maker is left with the squeezed apple pulp, known as pomace - traditionally fed to pigs and other livestock.

PROPOLIS Bee glue – collected by bees from sticky buds of trees and resin as it leaks from the bark. It is used to seal up cracks in the hive and stop draughts. It is also anti-bacterial and keeps the hive healthier.

QUEEN BEE The mother of the colony. A good queen will lay over 1,000 eggs a day in the spring and early summer.

SKEP Straw basket in which people once kept bees, still used today when taking a swarm.

SUPER Wooden box full of frames, added in the spring and summer when plenty of nectar is being brought in. The queen is kept out of supers which get filled with comb and honey by the worker bees. It is from these frames the beekeeper extracts honey.

SWARM Swarming is the natural reproduction of honey bee colonies. A new colony is formed when the resident queen bee leaves with a large group of worker bees (can be tens of thousands). A cast swarm is usually smaller and accompanied by a new virgin queen.

WORKER BEES The female workforce, all daughters of the queen bee. They do the cleaning, guard duties, fetching food and processing it, gathering water and propolis, feeding the grubs and queen… and more. When young they are house bees, when older they go out foraging.

The Interviews

The voices of beekeepers quoted are extracts from recordings and notes made by Kate Lynch during conversations in the field. The beekeepers have occasionally edited the transcripts of their spoken words. Therefore the quotations are a combination of verbatim speech and edits agreed with the beekeepers. The dates when the conversations took place are listed in the Directory.

A parallel project to interview beekeepers for the Somerset Voices Archive took place in the winter of 2010/2011, when Ann Heeley, in collaboration with Kate Lynch, recorded a large number of Somerset beekeepers.* Reference numbers of those interviews are included where appropriate.

The Somerset Voices Archive (oral recordings and written transcripts) is available for public reference at the Somerset Rural Life Museum, Glastonbury, and the Somerset Heritage Centre, Taunton. The archive also has its own website.

Somerset Rural Life Museum
Glastonbury
Somerset BA6 8DB
T 01458 831197
www.somerset.gov.uk/museums

Somerset Heritage Centre
Brunel Way
Norton Fitzwarren
Taunton TA2 6SF
T 01823 278805
www.somerset.gov.uk/archives

Somerset Voices website
www.somersetvoices.org.uk

* Ann Heeley has devoted much of her life to making archive recordings of Somerset farmers, tradesmen, and craftsmen and women. She has done this working as a volunteer at the Somerset Rural Life Museum. In 2010 she was awarded an MBE for this work.

Directory of beekeepers and their voices

Date of quoted conversation or interview with Kate Lynch (KL, page, date). Somerset voices archive interview with Ann Heeley (SV ref. no.).

TERRY ANDREWS *Rodney Stoke, Somerset*
Terry has been a hobbyist beekeeper for 40 years and was instrumental in developing the Wedmore & Cheddar Beekeepers Association. He has also been Introductory Course tutor and mentor. He keeps bees for interest in insects, relaxation and to satisfy his sweet tooth!
(KL p.29, 5.5.11: SV A\CMQ/2/658)

VICKY ANDREWS *Rodney Stoke, Somerset*
Vicky has been picking and enjoying flowers since the age of three – then it was buttercups. When given a small patch of garden aged eight, she grew and loved playing in amongst the 'giant' cosmos that her father gave her. Now she grows plants and flowers for wildlife, flower arranging and pleasure.
(KL p.29, 5.5.11: SV A\CMQ/2/658)

DANIEL BASTERFIELD *Colyton, Devon*
Daniel keeps 140 hives and is a second generation beekeeper, following his father. He relies on beekeeping for his income and is an occasional speaker and demonstrator at the Taunton Beekeepers Association which runs a permanent apiary at Heatherton Park.
www.the-apiary.co.uk

ELEANOR ROSE BURGESS *Staplehay, Taunton*
Eleanor is a third-generation beekeeper with 11 years' experience. She is the daughter of Rosemary Burgess and together they run around 20 hives with a small business selling honey, handmade soaps, beeswax candles, cosmetics, jams and jellies.
www.thebeekeepingladies.co.uk
(KL p.17, 9.3.11; p.19, 9.3.11; p.21, 16.4.10; p.57, 19.2.12: SV A\CMQ/2/620)

ROSEMARY BURGESS *Staplehay, Taunton*
Rosemary is an experienced, second-generation beekeeper. She has been Social Secretary for Taunton Beekeepers Association for several years (see ELEANOR ROSE above).
www.thebeekeepingladies.co.uk
(SV A\CMQ/2/621)

DAVID CHARLES *West Pennard, Somerset*
David is a retired teacher. He is a Master Beekeeper and has been involved with beekeeping and beekeeping education for 50 years. President of the British Beekeepers Association (1992–94) and Somerset Beekeepers Association (1986–89 and 1992–95).
(KL p.46, 13.9.11: SV A\CMQ/2/615)

COLIN AND JULIE COMBEN
Yeabridge, South Petherton, Somerset
Colin and Julie have run their smallholding, Honeypot Farm, since 2006, producing and selling honey, apple juice, cider and seasonal produce.
E thecombens@aol.com
T 07971 656440
(KL p.48, 15.9.11)

KAREN COX & CHRIS STRONG *Beer, Langport, Somerset*

Chris and Karen have planted apple, pear and plum trees to complement their established walnuts and perry pears. They see beekeeping as part of the stewardship of Nightingale Farm with their bees pollinating the fruit trees. They produce honey and other products from the hive and make a special traditional perry. www.nightingalefarm.com
(KL p.41 & 43, 21.7.10)

PETER DAVIES *Street, Somerset*

Peter has two years' experience as a beekeeper and runs three hives. One colony grew from the swarm he and Daniel Govier hived, illustrated on page 35. 'Beekeeping fits naturally with work on my smallholding where I grow top and soft fruit and vegetables.'

TOM DONE *Butleigh, Somerset*

Tom's interest in beekeeping began in the 1980s with one hive. On retiring from dairy farming he increased this to 12, keeping five at the Chalice Well Gardens, Glastonbury.
(KL p.14, 27.2.11: SV A\CMQ\2\662)

GERALD FISHER *Langport, Somerset*

Gerald has kept bees since the 1970s. He was Chief Steward of Bees and Honey at the Royal Bath & West Show for many years (for which he was made a Life Governor), Chairman of the Somerset Beekeepers Association (1999–2001) and President (2007–09). He has been Correspondence Tutor for the BBA, runs Introductory Courses in the county and gives practical demonstrations and talks.
(KL p.11, 14.2.12; p.30, 13.5.10: SV A\CMQ\2\638)

DANIEL GOVIER *Street, Somerset*

Daniel took up beekeeping four years ago. 'I developed a fascination with these amazing social insects and now run an orchard apiary. I'm hooked on the craft and try to learn as much as I can.' He is an active member of the Somerton and District Beekeepers Association. He also rears geese for Christmas. E dan.govier@talktalk.net
(KL p.34, 12.6.10; p.60, 17.12.11)

CHRISTIANE HARE *Rooksbridge, Somerset*
Christiane has been keeping bees with her husband, Michael, for 25 years. They have about ten hives and together run the Burnham-on-Sea Division of the Somerset Beekeepers Association which has increased from nine members to 40 in the last few years. (KL p.62, 12.3.12)

CHRIS HARRIES *Creech St. Michael, Somerset*
Chris started beekeeping in the mid-1970s and runs a successful bee farm. He rears colonies, runs a pollination service for local farmers, and makes traditional beeswax candles and polish. www.sedgemoorhoney.co.uk (KL p.45, 4.9.10: SV A\CMQ/2/646)

ANDREW HECKS *Street, Somerset*
Andrew runs the family cider farm with his brother Chris. He keeps his own bees which pollinate their fruit trees. They sell their honey alongside their farmhouse cider and other produce at their farm shop. www.hecksfarmhousecider.co.uk (KL p.24, 5.5.11)

EDDIE HOWE *Somerton, Somerset*
Eddie has been keeping bees for over 20 years and says he finds it as interesting as when he first started. He is an active member of the Somerton & District Beekeepers Association, taking a keen interest in the educational side. He sells honey and beeswax and also uses them in skincare products. 'If you have the interest, country living and beekeeping go hand in hand.' www.honeyshop.co.uk (KL p.27, 5.5.10)

PAT LEHAIN *Muchelney, Somerset*
Pat works as an ecologist and took up beekeeping seven years ago. One of his earliest memories was extracting honey with his grandfather, Phil Pugh, in Wales in the late 1960s and eating raw honeycomb fresh from the hive. 'I still find bees as fascinating as I did as a child, nearly half a century later. I have (and occasionally use) my grandfather's old smoker.' (KL p.22, 26.4.11)

ALEX MORRICE *Stoke St Gregory, Somerset*
Alex started beekeeping 20 years ago on retiring from the Royal Navy. He was Chairman of Somerset Beekeepers Association (2005–08), past Chairman and President of Somerton Beekeepers Association (still an active member) and gives talks on beekeeping and climate change. He and his wife, Sally, keep up to eight hives in their garden, next to pasture fields and hedgerows. E aandsmorrice@gmail.com (KL p.53, 9.2.12)

ADA OSTROUMOFF *Wincanton, Somerset*
Ada is seven and has been beekeeping at home with her mother, Alexandra, since the age of four. Alexandra runs a beekeeping club for Years Five and Six at Hazlegrove School, Sparkford, Somerset (www.hazlegrove.co.uk). www.snagfarm.co.uk (KL p.36, 22.1.12)

DIANA ROBERTSON *East Pennard, Somerset*
Diana has kept bees for 14 years and in the summer has eight or nine hives. The craft of skep-making used to go alongside beekeeping and Diana learnt to make a skep soon after becoming a beekeeper, originally to provide herself

with one in order to collect her own or a visiting swarm.
(KL p.58, 8.11.10: SV A\CMQ/2/642)

CHRIS STRONG *Beer, Langport, Somerset*
See Karen Cox above

NEIL TROOD *Long Sutton, Somerset*
Neil took up beekeeping as a hobby in the late 1970s with
his son, Timothy, and built up their apiary to almost 40
hives. At present they have reduced to only a few hives.
Neil was Chairman of the Somerset Beekeepers Association
(1996–98) and President (2001–03). He still maintains his
involvement with the County and the Taunton Division.
(KL p.12, 18.3.10; p.38, 3.7.11: SV A\CMQ/2/643)

ROY WHITE *Kingsbury Episcopi, Somerset*
An engineer in his working life, but always keen on
wildlife, Roy took up beekeeping when he retired twelve
years ago. He has become a specialist in rearing queens.
He sells honey, candles and other products made from
propolis, wax and honey.
(KL p.33, 14.6.11; p.50, 21.10.11: SV A\CMQ/2/639)

The following beekeepers were also recorded for the
Somerset Voices Archive (SV ref. no. in brackets).
CAROLINE BUTTER Draycott, Somerset (SV A\CMQ/2/644)
RICHARD CLARK Street, Somerset (SV A\CMQ/2/661)
KEN EDWARDS Spaxton, Somerset (SV A\CMQ/2/651)
SIMON JONES Creech St. Michael, Somerset (SV A\CMQ/2/654)
JOE KING Pilton, Somerset (SV A\CMQ/2/641)
MILNS PRISCOTT Milverton, Somerset (SV A\CMQ/2/656)

Links

The British Beekeepers Association

The British Beekeepers Association (BBKA) is an educational charity set up in 1874 and is the UK's leading organisation representing beekeepers. It promotes the importance of bees in the environment, supports beekeepers through the education necessary to maintain healthy colonies of honey bees, and raises awareness of the craft of beekeeping. On behalf of its members it lobbies Government, the EU and other official bodies on the importance of providing adequate funding for honeybee research.
www.bbka.org.uk

The Somerset Beekeepers Association

The Somerset Beekeepers Association (SBKA) was founded in 1906. It aims 'to advance the craft of apiculture, and promote and foster the education of its members, and of the public.'

The Association has a strong team of officers with their own specialist areas of expertise and there are currently 12 active Divisions of the Association in the county. The Association and its Divisions promote the craft of beekeeping – attending shows, producing newsletters, liaising with the press on matters of importance, organizing practical demonstrations and summer apiary meetings, and running beginners' and specialist classes to assist beekeepers in their management techniques. Full details of the SBKA and contact addresses of the 12 Somerset Divisions of the Association can be found on the web site.
www.somersetbeekeepers.org.uk

Bees for Development

Bees for Development works to promote the science and craft of beekeeping in developing countries. Beekeeping sustains the livelihoods of some of the poorest and most remote people in the world. Often these communities lack the information and support they need to protect and advance their craft. The charity also provides advice, training and education to beekeepers, helping them to earn more – often to pay for children's schooling and medical costs. Beekeeping is an effective way to create income from natural resources without damaging them. Bees ensure pollination of crops and wild vegetation, and thus help to maintain biodiversity.

Bees for Development is a small organisation set up in 1993, working worldwide from offices in Monmouth, Wales.
www.beesfordevelopment.org

Drawings and paintings by Kate Lynch

Afterword

One day in late spring by Eleanor Rose Burgess

On a hot day in late spring, half the colony of bees boils from the hive door, encouraging their queen to leave with them. They swirl around with an excited buzz, settling on a branch or bush while they decide where to go. The swarm sends out scout bees to house-hunt, and when they find a perfect space the mass takes flight and heads to its new home – perhaps a chimney stack, hollowed-out tree or a bait hive left out by a beekeeper. Once the bees have settled in, they hang in festoons and warm themselves up. This heat helps them convert the honey they gorged on before setting out, into wax which they secrete from their abdominal glands. In a few hours they can begin building comb. In a few days there will be racks of perfectly formed and uniform hexagonal cells in which their queen will lay eggs and create her female workforce. The colony has divided and is multiplying.

Back in the original colony reproduction had already been in the air before the queen took off. As spring brings hotter days and a good nectar flow, the bees get restless. They begin building larger 'drone' cells which the queen measures with her antennae and forelegs, and in each one she instinctively lays a male rather than a female egg. The bees may also build a very different type of cell, drooping downwards, a cell for the creation of a new virgin queen. This queen cell receives a female egg and, once it hatches, the larva is heavily fed a rich concoction of food. At the

same time, the worker bees put the old queen on a mean diet so she's light enough to fly. Then, when the new queen larva is big and fat and ready, the worker bees cap the cell. This is the trigger for the exodus and, on that hot late-spring day, half the bees in the colony swarm, taking their old queen with them.

Those bees that stay put are anticipating their emerging queen. She makes noises from inside her cell and the workers thin the wax so she can more easily chew her way out. There may be more than one new queen. The first to emerge will often sting and kill her queen sisters through the cell walls – safer to do this than face a rival in open combat. The winning queen, however, is still a virgin, she is no use to the colony until she mates.

Meanwhile, the male drones have been emerging too. These big lads are being well looked after. The female worker bees even welcome and feed visiting drones from other colonies at this time of year. Every sunny day the male bees fly from the hive, heading to 'drone congregation' areas – known places where, year after year, the drones and new virgin queens assemble. The drones lazily buzz about until a virgin queen turns up, then they tail her, comet-like, jostling to get a chance to mate. After each drone is successful he dies, and the newly-mated queen returns to her hive to begin her egg-laying life.

In each colony, new or old, from spring through to late summer, the queen is laying eggs. Generally the cells she finds are girl-size for girl eggs – to produce worker bees to keep the workforce going. After three days, each girl egg hatches into a grub and young worker bees feed it with nutritious brood food they secrete from their glands. The female grub grows up fast. Six days after hatching out she is fat and ready to pupate. Her older sisters cap her cell with wax so she can spin her cocoon in safety. Twelve days later she emerges as a fully-formed worker bee.

Newborn the worker bee is hairy – it is all the hard work she now has to do which will turn her bald. Her first job is housework – cleaning up cells before the queen lays another egg. Then, as her brood-food glands develop, she becomes a nurse bee, feeding her larval sisters. After this, she will pack nectar and pollen into cells, collecting it from foraging bees as they return to the hive, then evaporating the nectar's excess water to turn it into honey. As her sting gland develops she'll start guard duties, protecting the hive from robbers or invaders, like the yellow-jacketed wasp. Eventually our worker bee is old enough and strong enough to head out on foraging trips. On her maiden flight she spirals upwards and away from the hive entrance, making a mental map of the area so she will be able to navigate her way home. She seeks the most food-rich flowers as close as possible to the colony, but she might travel over a mile. Finding a good quantity of sugar-rich nectar or nutritious pollen will result in enthusiastic dancing when she returns to the hive.

These dances involve intricate, shimmying figure-of-eight patterns which explain to her fellow worker bees where the food source is, how worthwhile it is and what it tastes like – samples may be given out to encourage fellow workers to get out and forage! At the height of the flower season there will be many thousands of foraging female workers in each colony.

This massive operation to gather food is to feed the colony, not just through the summer, but also through the long flowerless winter. With other bee species only the queen lives through the winter and in the spring she has to forage and build cells for her larvae unaided. Honey bees are different. The honey bee queen is helpless on her own, unable to produce wax or forage for herself, so she needs her worker bees – and it takes a considerable store of honey and pollen to get queen and workers through the winter.

As autumn draws in, the number of bees in the colony diminishes – the queen lays fewer eggs, so many of the short-lived summer worker bees are not replaced. Drones are banished from the hive, violently kept out, killed by the guard bees if they dare re-enter – they would eat through the precious food stores if they lived.

In the cold days of winter honey bees survive by congregating into a dense ball and forming the winter cluster. By vibrating her thorax a single bee can create heat. In their thousands they keep the core of the winter cluster at a constant temperature, each worker bee taking her turn on the outside of the ball where she will cool down, almost to death, before heading inside the cluster to heat

up again. The queen, mother of the entire colony, remains warm in the centre. She is the only bee who can lay fertilized eggs – if she does not make it through the winter the colony will die out.

The first warmth and flowers of spring bring the ageing worker bees out, collecting pollen to feed the young larvae already fattening in the hive – for the queen has started to lay again. And, as the number of bees in the colony grows, on a hot day in late spring half the bees boil from the entrance to the hive, encouraging their queen to go with them… the colony is about to divide and multiply.

Acknowledgements

This book has been a team effort. The beekeepers are the authors, telling their own seasonal stories. They showed me the rudiments of the ancient craft of beekeeping, letting me know when they were opening or moving a hive, adding a super, taking a swarm or spinning out honey, and inviting me to orchards, small-holdings, moors and into their sheds. Thanks to all the beekeepers featured and many others who have been very helpful along the way. It has been a fascinating journey into another world only a few miles from where I live on the Somerset Levels.

I am grateful for the support of the Somerset Beekeepers Association and local Divisions of the Association. I particularly enjoyed the Divisional meetings and their hospitality (I can recommend their splendid tea and cakes which I understand beekeeping meetings are renowned for). I have also appreciated help from the British Beekeepers Association, as well as a grant from the Somerset Levels and Moors Local Action for Rural Communities (LARC) and The Elmgrant Trust.

Thanks to the staff of the Somerset Rural Life Museum, Glastonbury, and New Brewery Arts, Cirencester for their contributions. I am glad that Ann Heeley made recordings of many Somerset beekeepers for the Somerset Voices Archive as part of this project and it was good to work together again.

It is a pleasure to give a special mention to the Bees for Development Trust and I am grateful to their patron, broadcaster Martha Kearney, herself a passionate beekeeper, for taking time out of her busy life to write the foreword to the book.

Thanks to Rosemary and Eleanor Rose Burgess for their encouragement from the beginning; David Charles, who kept a colony in a traditional skep for a season in order to demonstrate the old art of driving bees; Sue Young, for her finely-tuned help with editing; Richard Sainsbury at Delmar Studio; Lyn Davies, the designer of this book; Steve Rose at Hampton Printing; my husband, James; also Roj and Caroline Wholey for their welcome – it was their tree which that fine swarm settled in long enough for Roy to collect it.

Last but not least, a toast – to the miracle in the hive and a long and healthy future for the honey bee.

KATE LYNCH
2012

A beekeeper doesn't really keep bees – they'll always be wild – all we do is offer them a nice home in the hope they won't run away ALEX MORRICE

Kate Lynch (née Armstrong) lives in Somerset with her husband, painter James Lynch. She often takes rural farming and craft work as the subject for her paintings and drawings and she collects related conversations.

This book follows *Willow* (ISBN 978 0 9544394 0 6) & *Sheep, from Lamb to Loom* (ISBN 978 0 9544394 2 2). www.katelynch.co.uk

I can just smell a bit of venom

Steven
hanging in chains
they're the wax moving
you can tell by the way
they're bagging

a cluster of beekeepers.